Adventure Book 2

By David Kalvitis

First Edition

Rochester, www.monkeyingaround.com **New York**

Adventure Book 2

By David Kalvitis

First Edition

**Monkeying Around
PO Box 10131
Rochester, New York 14610 USA
585-256-2660
800-553-4300
Fax: 585-442-2965
info@monkeyingaround.com
www.monkeyingaround.com**

Rochester, **New York**

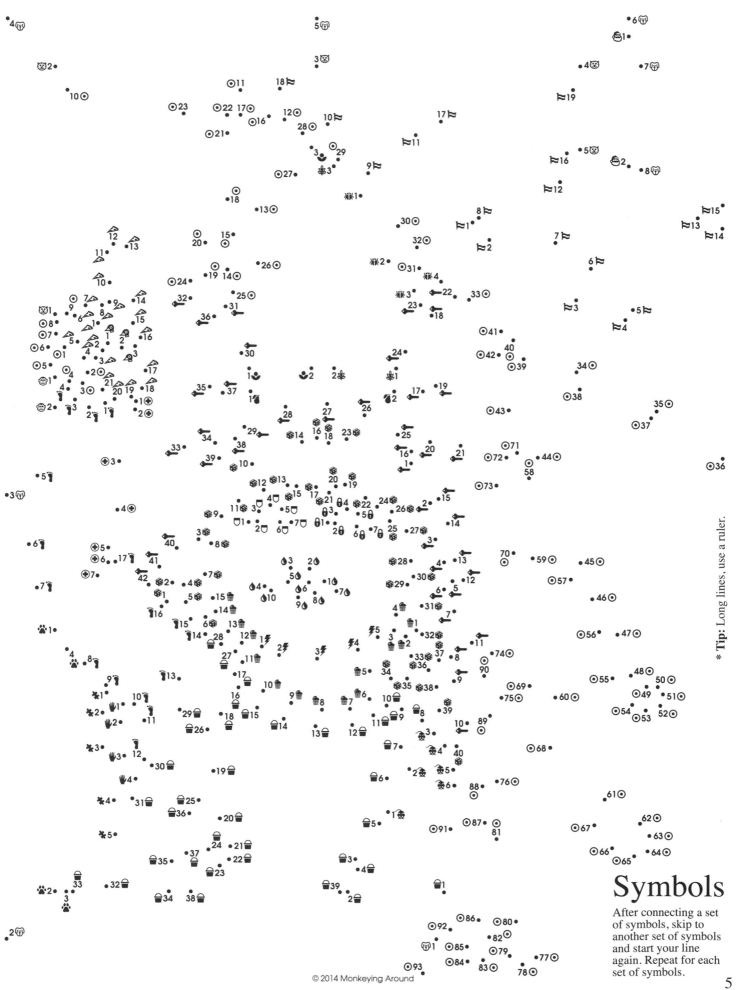

Symbols

After connecting a set of symbols, skip to another set of symbols and start your line again. Repeat for each set of symbols.

* **Tip:** Long lines, use a ruler.

5

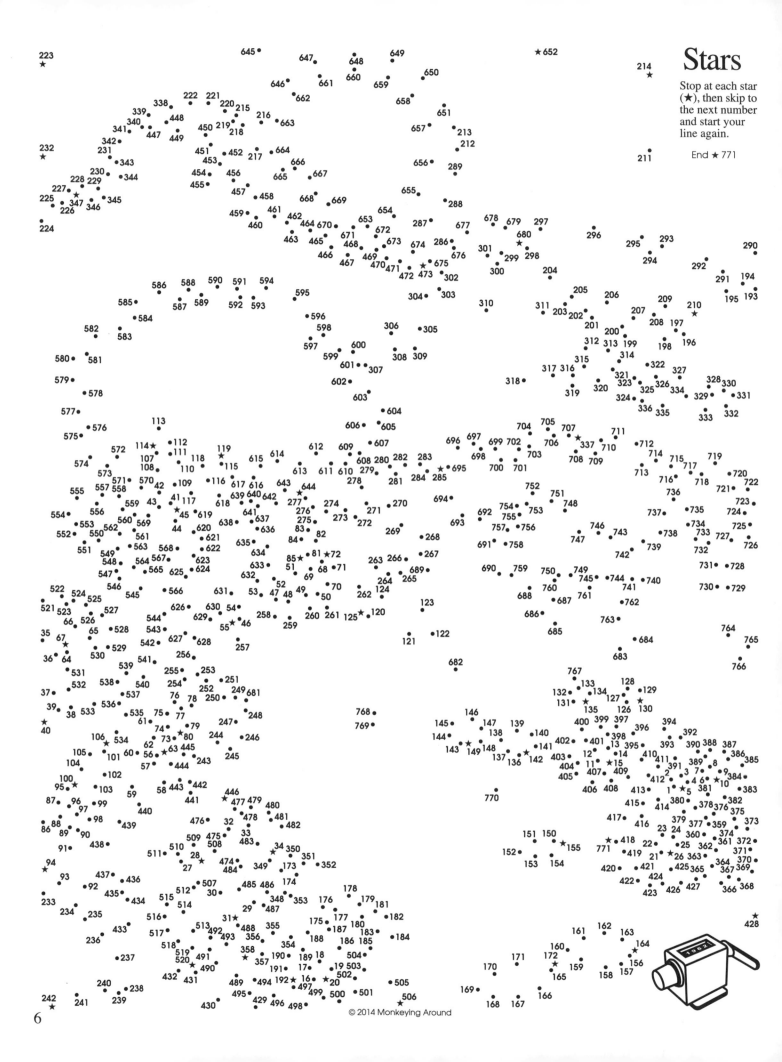

Stars

Stop at each star
(★), then skip to
the next number
and start your
line again.

End ★ 771

© 2014 Monkeying Around

6

Stars

Stop at each star
(★), then skip to
the next number
and start your
line again.

End ★ 434

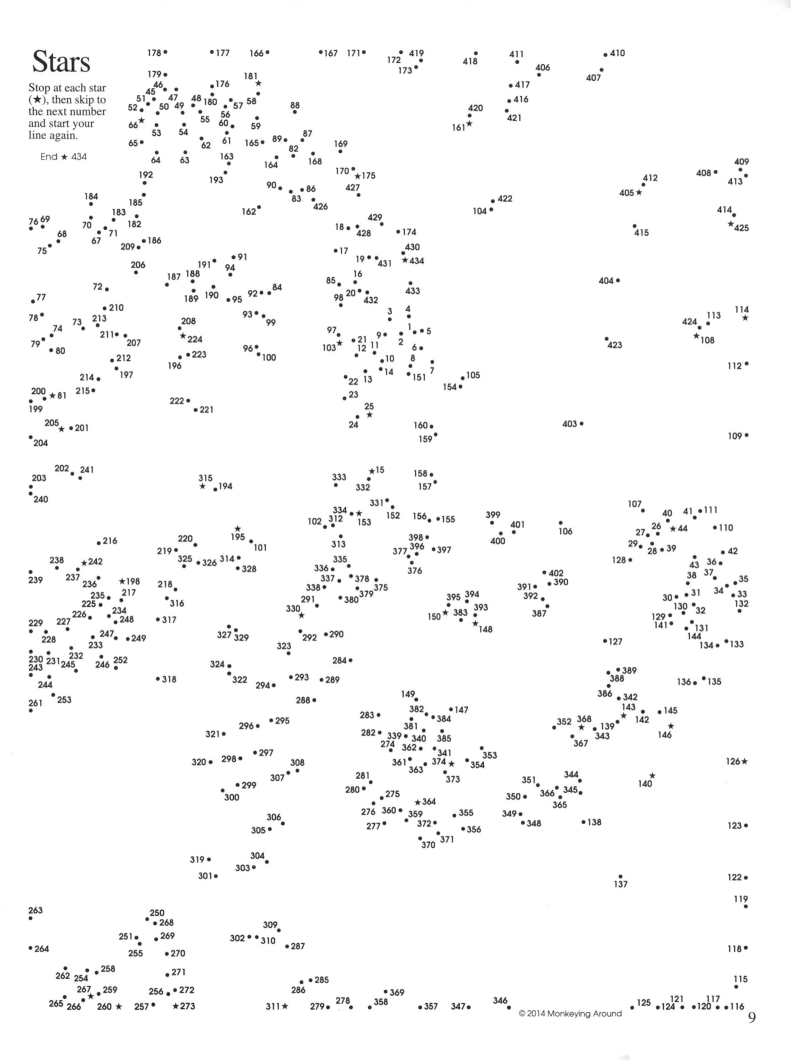

9

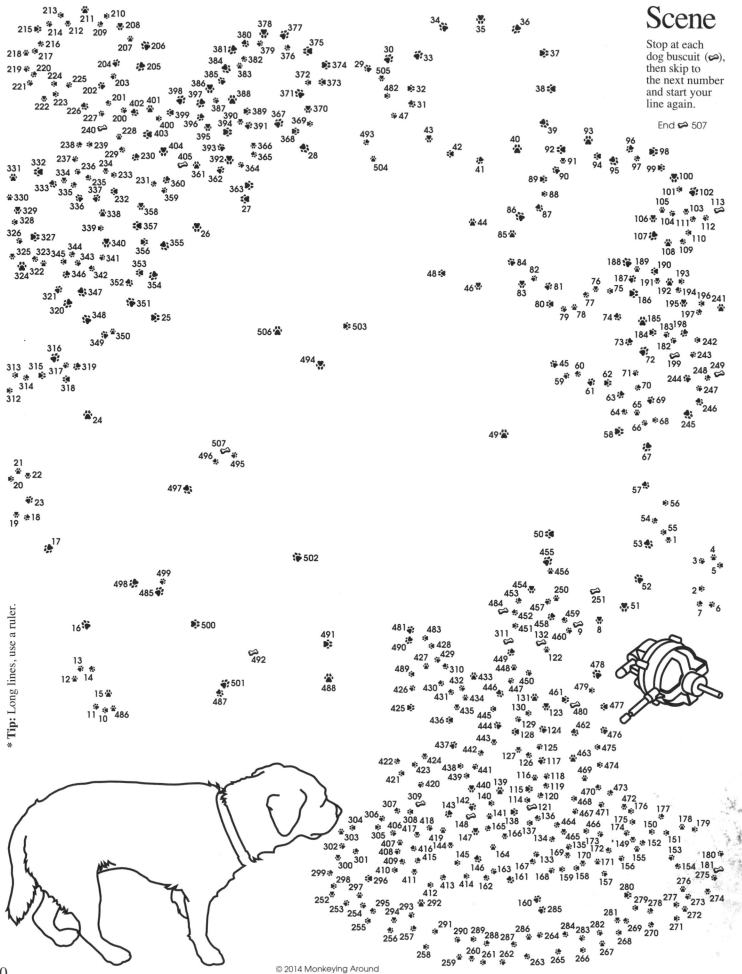

Scene

Stop at each dog buscuit (🦴), then skip to the next number and start your line again.

End 🦴 507

Tip: Long lines, use a ruler.

10

© 2014 Monkeying Around

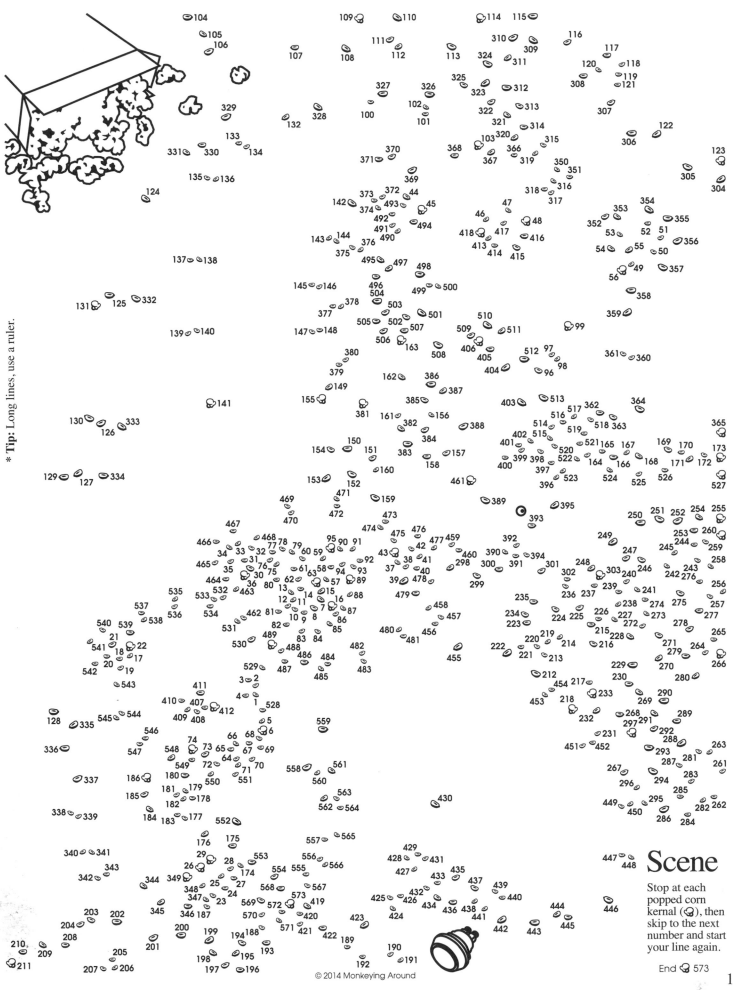

Scene

Stop at each popped corn kernal (🌽), then skip to the next number and start your line again.

End 🌽 573

*Tip: Long lines, use a ruler.

11

Odd/Even

Connect Dots:
odd numbers only
● 1 − 549
even numbers only
● 2 − 614

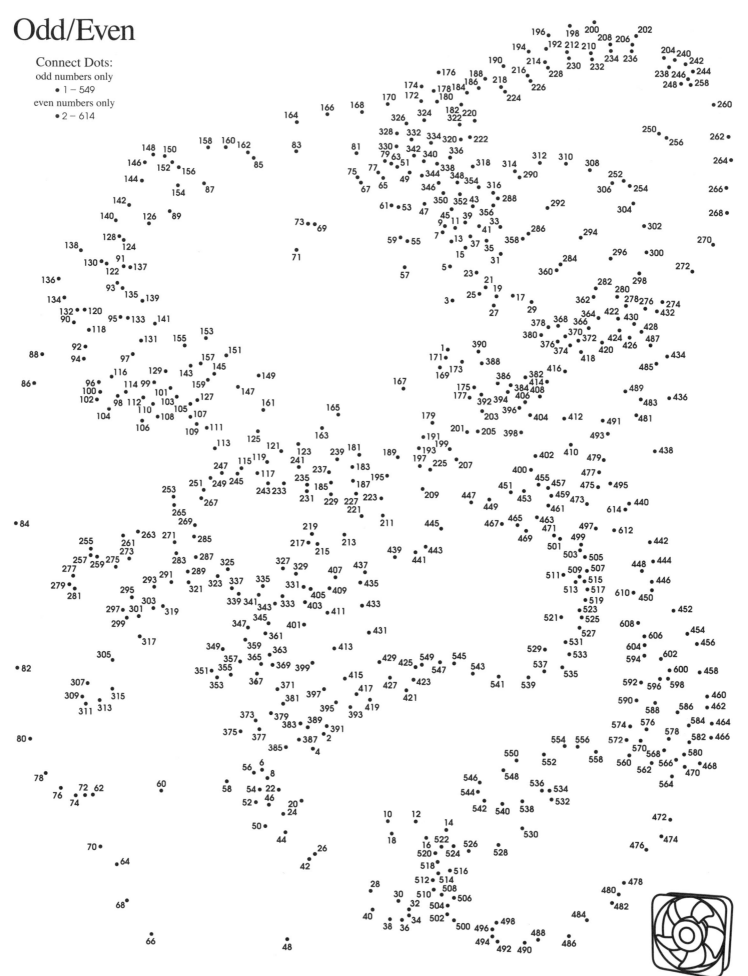

Crazy Dots

Connect Dots:

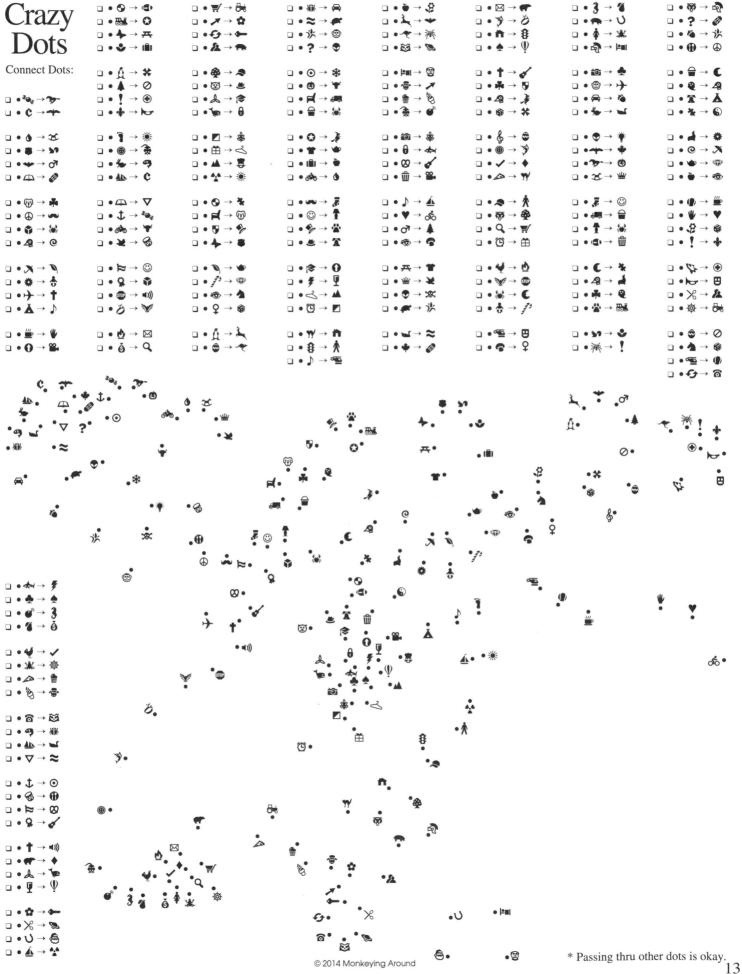

* Passing thru other dots is okay.

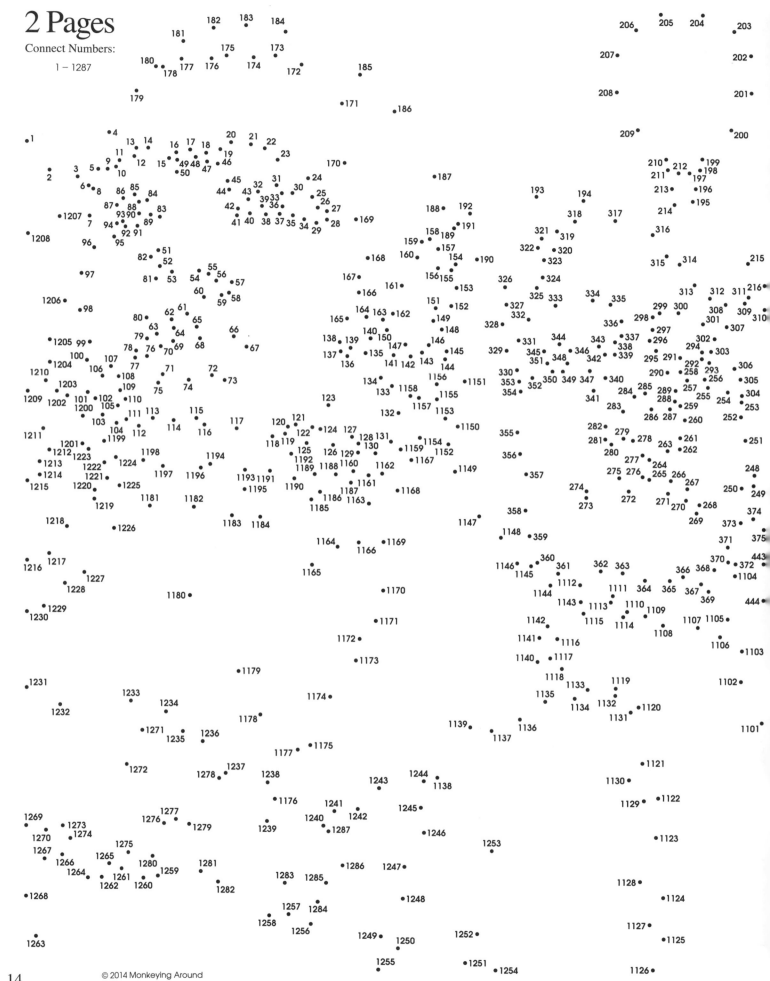

15

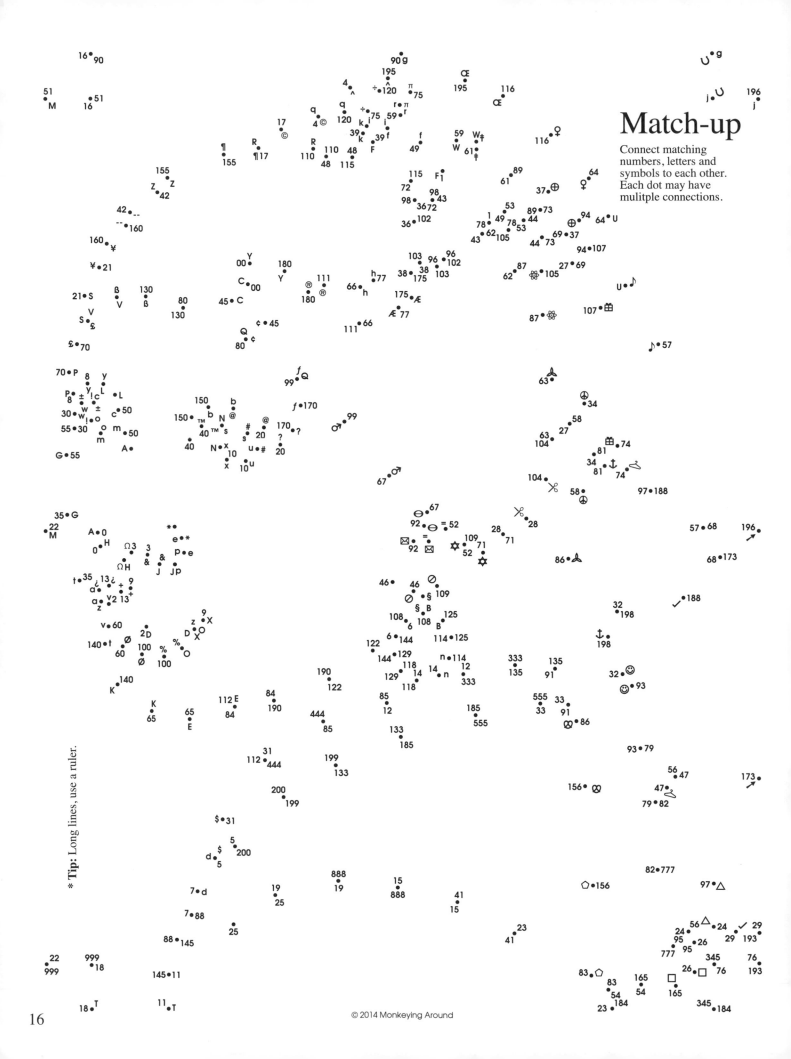

Match-up

Connect matching numbers, letters and symbols to each other. Each dot may have mulitple connections.

*Tip: Long lines, use a ruler.

© 2014 Monkeying Around

16

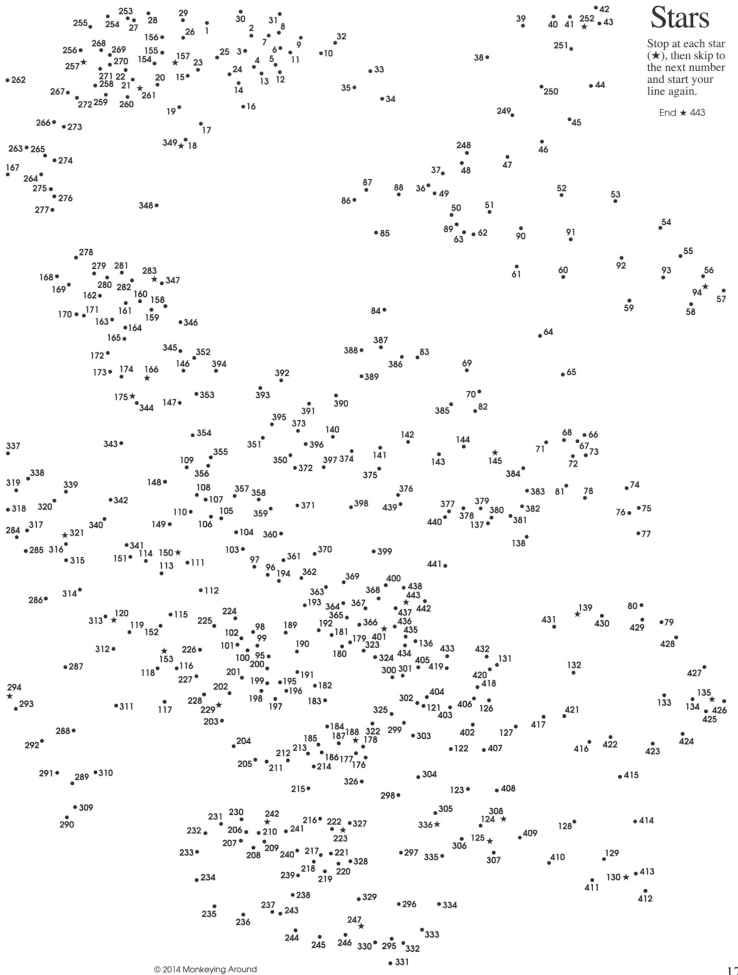

Stars

Stop at each star (★), then skip to the next number and start your line again.

End ★ 443

Coordinates

Find the dot at each set of coordinates. Connect each dot to the next, making one continuous line. "x" numbers run up the side, "y" across the bottom. Use a corner of paper to make finding coordinates and dots easier.

Start Here!	x:30, y:26	x:03, y:33	x:04, y:35	x:05, y:35	x:17, y:31	x:18, y:32	x:16, y:34
	x:15, y:34	x:14, y:33	x:13, y:33	x:17, y:37	x:18, y:37	x:16, y:35	x:19, y:33
	x:20, y:34	x:21, y:34	x:18, y:31	x:20, y:30	x:21, y:32	x:23, y:32	x:22, y:30
	x:21, y:30	x:28, y:28	x:30, y:28	x:30, y:36	x:28, y:35	x:29, y:35	x:29, y:34
	x:26, y:32	x:25, y:30	x:24, y:30	x:27, y:35	x:28, y:36	x:27, y:36	x:21, y:35

x:28, y:37	x:30, y:38	x:28, y:56	x:29, y:56	x:30, y:55	x:31, y:40	x:31, y:28	x:32, y:28	x:32, y:30	x:33, y:30	x:34, y:31
x:34, y:32	x:32, y:34	x:32, y:39	x:37, y:47	x:39, y:45	x:36, y:50	x:32, y:48	x:32, y:49	x:34, y:52	x:41, y:54	x:41, y:53
x:40, y:52	x:38, y:51	x:40, y:47	x:39, y:50	x:41, y:50	x:42, y:49	x:42, y:48	x:41, y:46	x:43, y:43	x:42, y:41	x:44, y:43
x:47, y:44	x:47, y:43	x:46, y:42	x:38, y:38	x:38, y:39	x:40, y:42	x:41, y:42	x:40, y:44	x:39, y:44	x:33, y:37	x:33, y:35
x:35, y:33	x:35, y:31	x:33, y:28	x:50, y:40	x:50, y:38	x:49, y:37	x:33, y:27	x:33, y:26	x:46, y:09	x:45, y:08	x:44, y:08
x:32, y:25	x:31, y:25	x:19, y:00	x:18, y:02	x:18, y:03	x:30, y:25	x:24, y:19	x:22, y:20	x:20, y:25	x:19, y:26	x:18, y:26
x:15, y:25	x:12, y:22	x:16, y:23	x:18, y:25	x:19, y:25	x:16, y:22	x:14, y:21	x:13, y:19	x:13, y:16	x:16, y:17	x:21, y:21
x:21, y:20	x:16, y:16	x:14, y:15	x:15, y:14	x:18, y:15	x:23, y:18	x:19, y:15	x:14, y:13	x:12, y:13	x:10, y:16	x:10, y:17
x:13, y:21	x:12, y:21	x:10, y:18	x:09, y:18	x:10, y:22	x:11, y:24	x:10, y:26	x:09, y:26	x:08, y:25	x:08, y:24	x:09, y:24
x:08, y:23	x:07, y:24	x:07, y:25	x:11, y:30	x:12, y:30	x:10, y:27	x:12, y:25	x:15, y:29	End Here!		

* **Tips:** Long lines, use ruler. Circling dots helps.

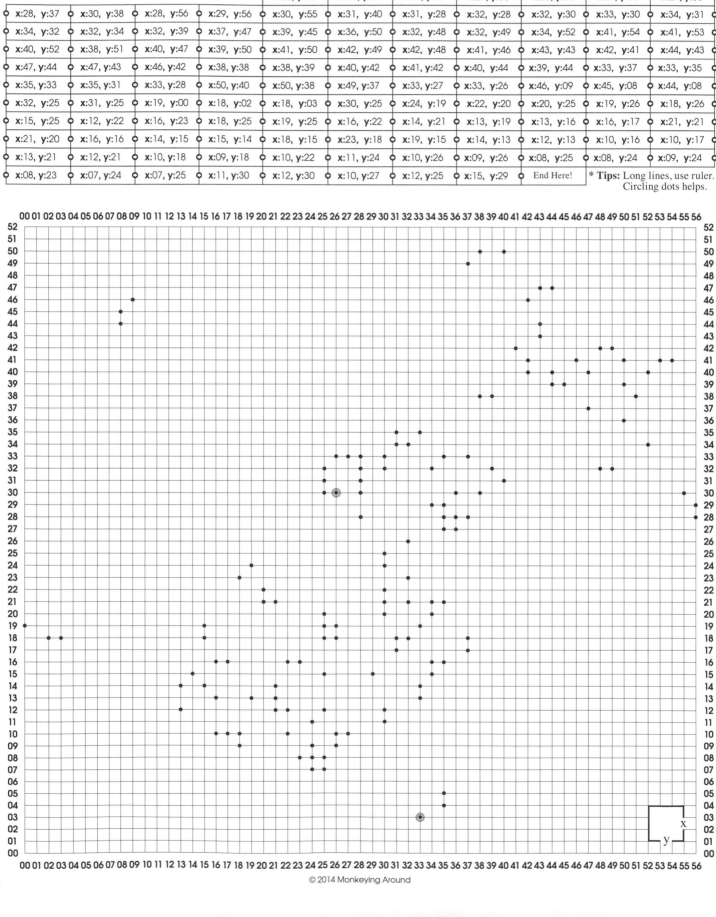

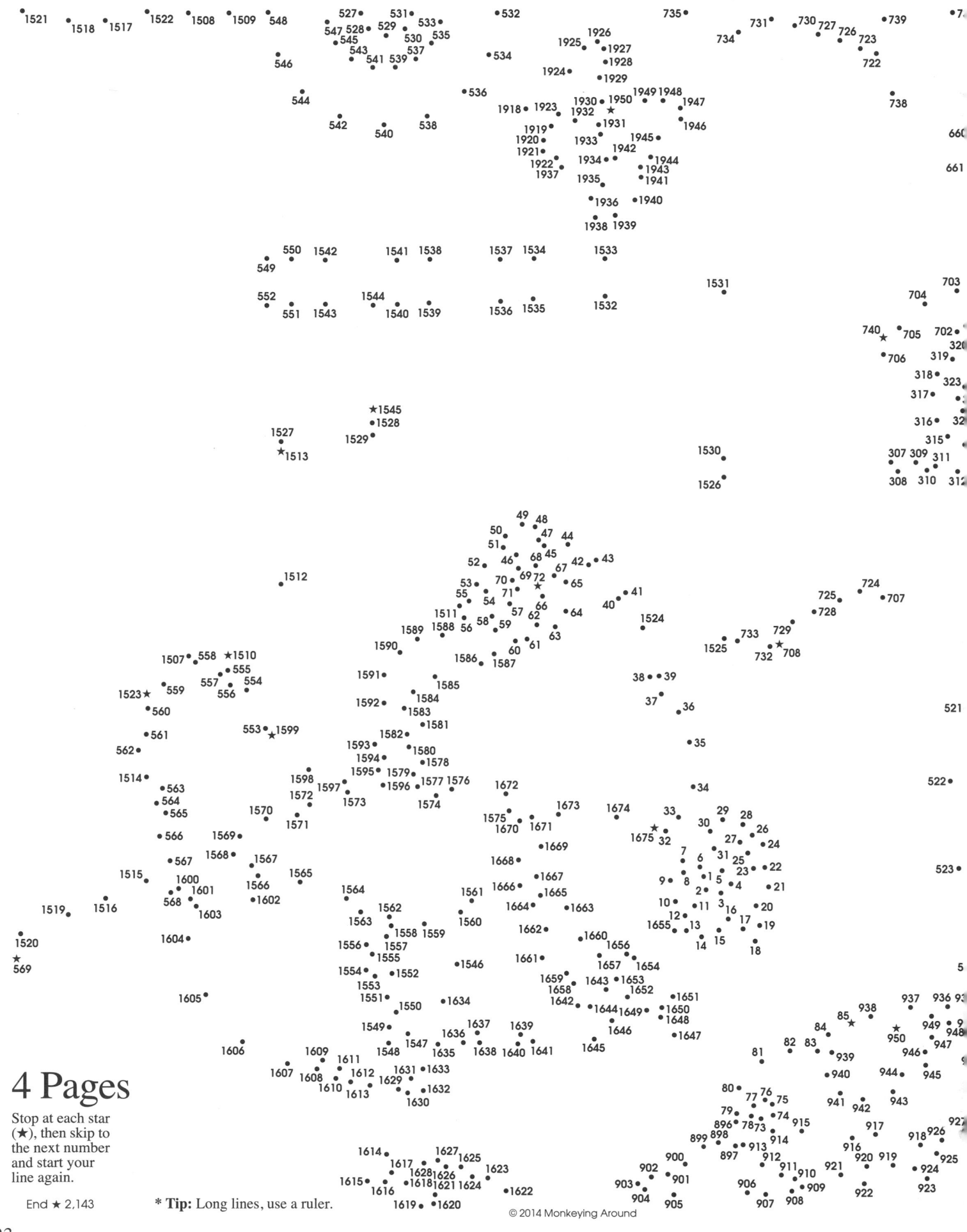

4 Pages

Stop at each star (★), then skip to the next number and start your line again.

End ★ 2,143

* **Tip:** Long lines, use a ruler.

© 2014 Monkeying Around

23

★1399
•1398
★•1397
1396
1394 •1395
1416 1417
•1418
•32
33
638
112★ 34
111 379 1479 1480
109 110 37 35
38 378 380★
42★ 39 36
41 1471 1472
40 1470 1501 189
1469 375
1468 178 192 193
1467 1499 191 194
1500 179 190
180 ★196 195 376
1412
181 369 372
1411 1410 370 371 373
1407 1409 374★
1408 ★721 1586

633 527★ 521
•634
635 526 523★ 558
636 524•522
1477 1476 1475 525 1525★ 559 ★563
1478 562 517
560 561 520★

1473
1474 1504 1524 1520 1519
1503 1522 1521 518 1518
1502 1523 519 578/579
183 1505 581 580
188 1506 582
187 184 185 1583
186 182 1507 584 585
1508 583 1582
1509 1510 1584 1581
1511★ 1585
1580

708• 1579
•709
21 125 1413
124 1406 1546 1547
•23 126 1545 1548
★ 127 1527 1528 1578
128 1438 1544 1529 1549
•715 551 1437 1526 1550
717 1435 1439 1543 1541 1530
718 719 1436 1561★ 1542 1540 1577
720 362 363 1444 1443 1442 1590 1589 1496 1497 1531 1551
547 548 364 365 366 367 1449 1560 1513
557 368★ 1587 1445 1446 1450 1495 1498★ 1539 1532 1514
549 550 556 1451 1559 1538 1552 1576
546• 555 1452 1537 1533 1515
353★ 545 552 553 554 1558 1536 1557 1535 1534 1553 1575
1343 1588 355 354 1556 1555 1554
•352 544 1434 1441 1494 1566 1568
1432 1433 1440 356 1493 1567 1517★•1574
•351 1431 1445 1562 502 501 505 506 500 1573
•1430 1453 868 869 1490 1491 1572
350•1429 1454 1455 871 1563 486 538 499 1569 1570 1571
•1370 870 872 1564 492 536 537 1485 1486
21 1369 1367 1366 867 456 487 535 494 493 498 497
22 1368 1363 1364 1365 873 1457 1565 361 503 495 496 490
1362 866 874 1458 488 504 539 358
361 865 1459 360 489 359
864 1461 490 357
876 1462 491 358
1463 543 528 529 530
1464 1481 540 533 532 531
1465 1482 1483 1484 488 487 485 486

3 Pages

Stop at each star
(★), then skip to
the next number
and start your
line again.

End ★ 1590

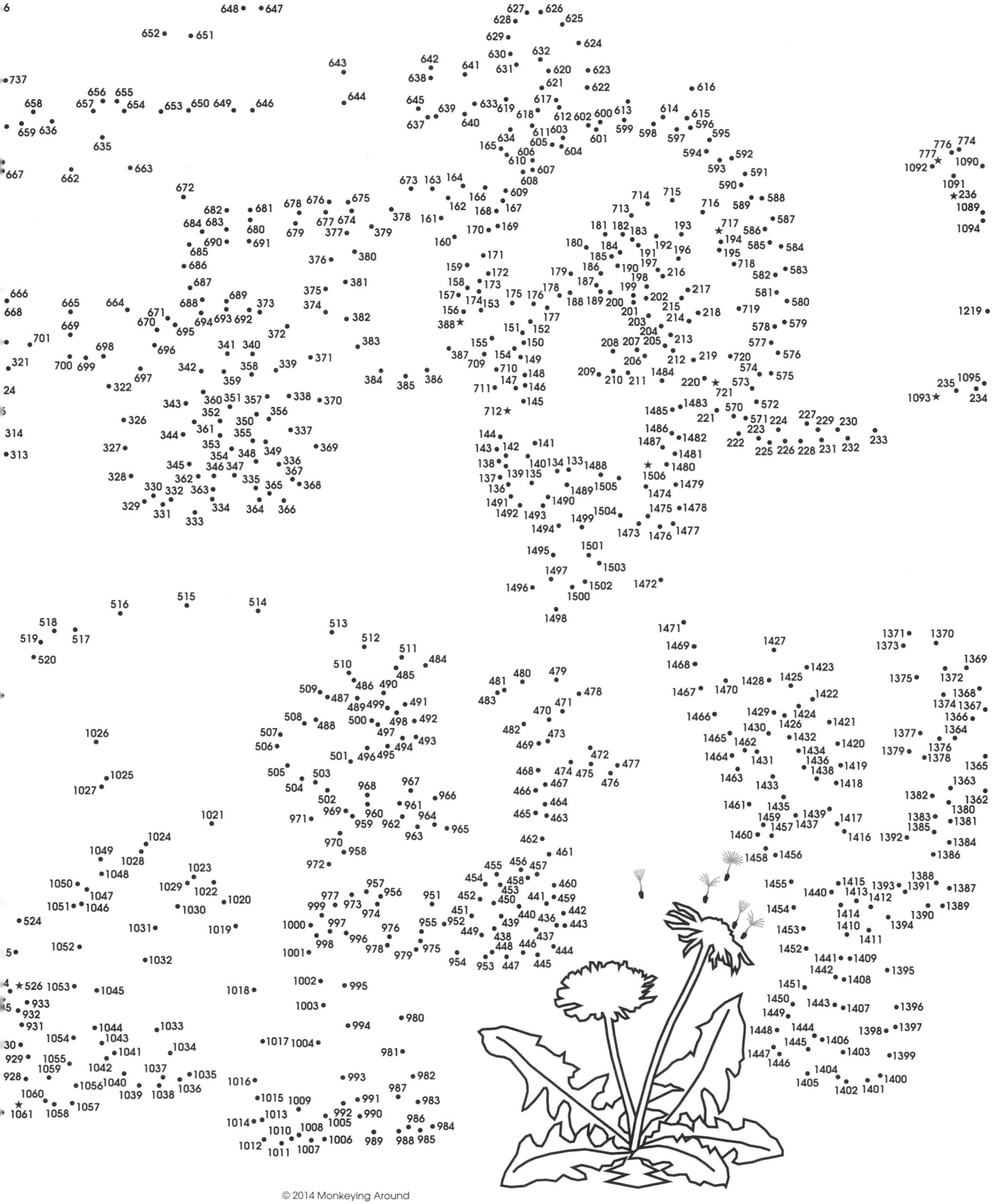

3 Pages

Stop at each star
(★), then skip to
the next number
and start your
line again.

End ★ 1239

* **Tip:** Long lines, use a ruler.

© 2014 Monkeying Around

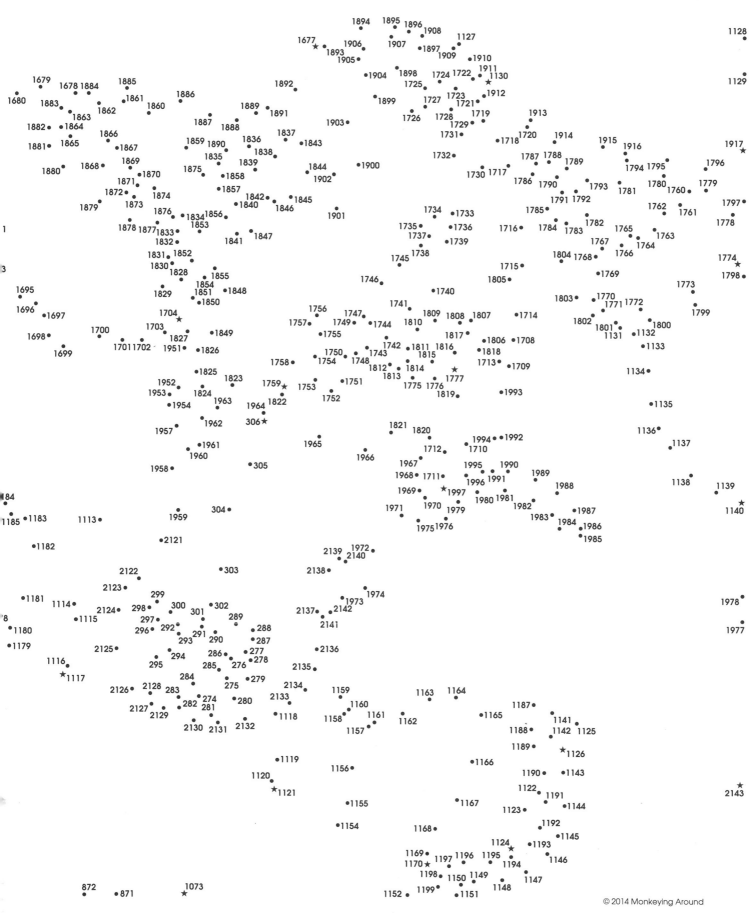

26

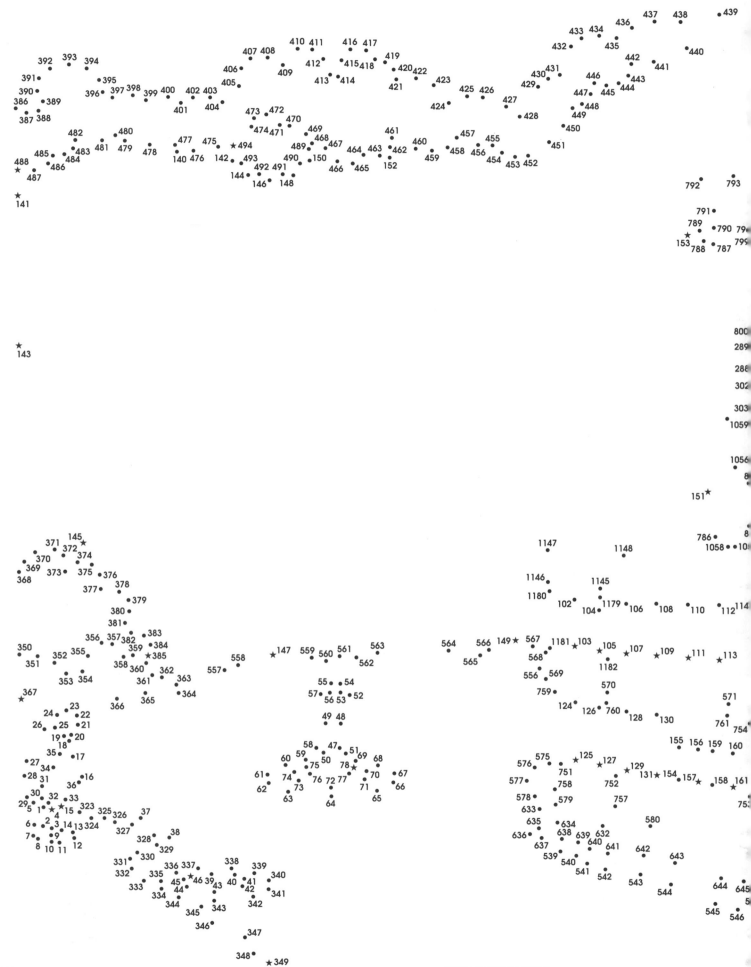

© 2014 Monkeying Around

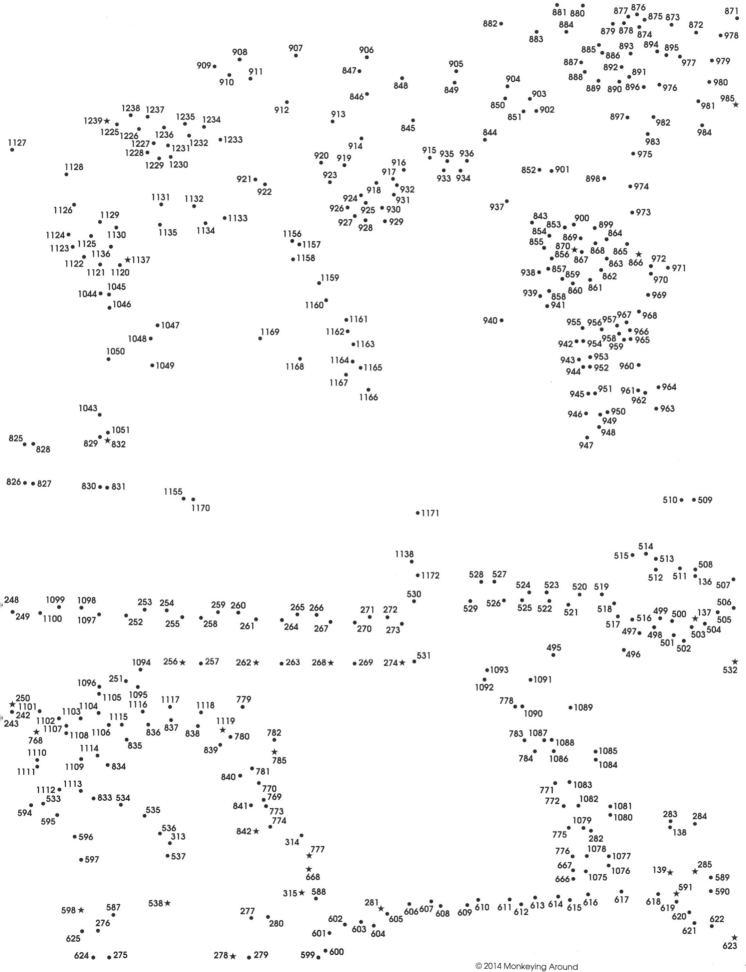

29

Alpha Dots

Start with the word "ace", and connect all the words in alphabetical order, ending with the word "zoo".

ace
rub
act
beg
row
run
bat
rip
bed
big
add
bag
rut
age
air
axe
old
rib
sad
sea
saw
rye
awe
ant
oil
red
she
ate
ape
one
sew
bin
off
opt
ran
rat
shy
tux
ash
arm
zip
odd
orb
sip
tea
zig
yes
box
oat
six
sky
tub
two
zoo
oar
ore
rag
toe
toy
ten
tap
urn
yet
yam
boy
son
tip
tie
art
you
yak
out
tad
zap
put
spy
sun
van
wow
wry
bug
vex
wag
why
win
bun
use
who
won
pal
vat
vow
was
wig
bus
oak
nut
nap
pup
cab
paw
pry
web
nag
lid
pea
pot
pop
way
nun
net
pin
bye
cup
mut
lip
pie
key
new
let
pen
can
now
pet
kit
kid
mug
leg
kin
cub
car
lit
keg
cut
nib
lab
mud
led
cat
nod
log
cry
not
mob
jar
lay
dad
cot
mom
lot
jug
cog
nil
mix
jam
jaw
cow
mid
mop
day
met
low
joy
jag
jay
ivy
jet
job
lug
jot
den
men
map
mad
ion
irk
fun
jig
fog
dew
dog
dot
imp
ink
dig
dip
dye
duo
dry
ilk
hum
inn
fox
fly
eel
ear
due
ice
hug
hot
gas
gal
fry
fix
fig
ewe
eat
had
era
egg
hit
gel
few
end
elf
ego
get
fed
fad
him
hay
guy
gnu
eye
elm
hid
hat
gum
far
hex
hen
got
gob
fan

© 2014 Monkeying Around

30

Numbers

Start at the circled number 001. Connect numbers in sequential order, passing through extra numbers. End at circled 210.

761 464 356 564 266 662 862 388 533 893 368 699 912 716 406 426 609 523 416 457 668 833 937 712

811 903 908 684 561 468 879 200 650 201 584 596 449 351 685 992 807 510 638 506 496 734 602 384

633 514 445 276 420 600 688 566 424 665 990 202 372 599 378 813 645 996 816 798 568 453 746 442

465 546 428 924 827 264 199 277 987 489 952 608 972 853 723 647 919 882 949 284 858 382 406 905

968 851 622 390 758 854 755 438 846 950 534 802 502 528 837 593 406 652 417 435 586 376 697 404

482 778 545 353 477 794 927 840 206 804 205 654 874 773 964 826 740 904 413 572 895 431 291 808

419 676 803 547 574 014 526 412 207 721 959 204 425 203 559 782 430 849 521 705 535 916 804 605 693 802 549 891 644 978

616 405 784 015 905 614 595 013 601 869 728 (210) 399 582 790 625 466 005 776 956 482 274 501 515 701 422 909 703 379 747

809 731 984 427 768 994 686 867 012 208 209 009 571 008 497 006 884 186 004 787 361 657 232 800 508 744 507 400 863 730

646 926 745 777 366 649 198 763 856 611 780 768 931 841 007 187 866 185 003 433 642 263 513 914 403 886 365 576 910 488

562 423 016 812 515 715 831 630 552 011 010 427 984 776 188 184 (001) 002 733 605 759 885 726 907 708 509 448 999 896 631

754 460 906 493 971 197 796 853 498 191 469 192 189 588 675 785 366 474 935 985 358 218 842 974 233 682 792 474 658 923

696 017 724 835 555 485 583 475 986 663 426 918 700 855 575 715 183 639 666 579 815 423 965 445 381 386 459 570 890 671

364 844 947 196 883 445 453 703 190 667 573 797 917 604 727 179 752 932 177 789 176 730 222 615 379 878 626 902 766 478

664 018 719 874 195 706 631 501 193 473 126 948 872 180 538 750 178 876 653 751 174 175 629 893 231 966 541 437 581 771

491 118 619 749 580 948 194 872 125 411 260 127 262 128 181 182 377 265 172 173 268 899 518 637 532 701 212 829 993 591

553 364 119 908 120 371 939 124 523 257 447 503 242 241 902 910 635 463 171 872 818 267 976 587 393 825 904 439 732 527

998 836 455 019 404 967 748 123 254 255 560 883 920 239 055 129 467 234 925 636 473 547 508 946 805 669 756 632 957 410

117 531 900 592 951 121 122 512 325 252 249 243 240 056 401 237 235 278 167 520 935 775 165 857 471 690 472 272 563 285

937 962 921 469 290 588 023 022 251 250 408 247 484 057 238 130 788 329 273 462 170 576 819 824 164 929 779 446 413 551

116 714 656 375 787 672 583 024 820 960 911 021 765 244 245 770 641 961 451 166 271 981 494 270 915 163 901 797 767 259

795 367 940 608 906 597 628 769 680 760 345 839 246 229 230 928 516 490 650 282 930 456 145 383 409 394 875 533 969 357

360 115 507 673 458 860 774 888 025 020 470 610 228 227 709 504 799 369 168 762 283 144 619 678 146 548 783 946 694 852

660 913 114 497 261 529 356 602 781 058 651 934 220 221 867 226 408 750 835 169 287 374 743 398 421 868 603 954 355 543

963 838 495 859 113 112 558 387 786 791 936 537 627 965 567 380 656 397 280 723 407 143 418 793 139 147 958 162 655 360

880 540 870 970 850 846 500 901 713 059 629 798 099 213 834 951 452 611 429 661 593 659 933 140 681 138 524 772 440 810

735 814 483 668 441 111 698 060 026 517 864 100 538 098 627 097 668 585 922 132 683 288 945 432 707 613 687 909 161 577

742 557 873 565 717 979 584 711 938 027 544 368 657 729 861 621 481 131 606 481 520 443 142 141 733 385 592 832 643 719

898 590 110 824 408 061 763 803 546 975 718 101 618 207 211 596 809 223 359 490 153 876 435 977 617 528 137 789 394 822

724 536 109 702 350 696 468 395 995 542 482 973 351 279 997 096 710 054 741 989 286 429 133 692 134 800 386 148 700 281

108 568 881 905 866 443 613 675 706 738 813 433 626 878 275 210 214 217 216 691 894 326 152 991 548 135 136 883 806 160

597 370 822 742 942 692 988 833 103 577 102 380 621 897 095 208 530 215 053 595 712 289 705 363 759 526 668 358 939 420

950 536 745 493 971 383 953 707 643 941 525 029 087 088 375 716 209 785 753 485 623 292 154 635 415 605 985 149 734 628

107 370 431 932 353 624 104 062 554 028 428 520 030 089 094 093 953 051 052 428 736 293 523 830 151 784 575 815 472 159

253 106 762 534 105 035 034 983 754 980 086 514 902 989 739 883 763 050 687 922 735 571 691 607 574 696 150 480 948 651

664 409 248 507 502 720 814 546 499 635 402 031 952 504 092 944 458 756 352 598 612 943 294 481 155 423 751 730 158 538

491 979 528 749 927 423 631 415 817 085 567 090 091 354 822 867 206 986 432 442 402 506 496 384 602 522 156 157 541 973

550 465 036 623 404 064 740 063 033 032 046 380 367 397 049 403 380 873 408 459 602 295 391 422 746 400 579 818 510 976

514 836 757 625 065 813 942 084 408 533 753 743 048 923 532 624 902 825 989 381 296 707 473 373 980 640 636 436 736 508

709 684 517 625 524 529 424 663 074 960 806 047 885 585 960 982 627 413 593 894 432 912 586 382 674 476 562 725 529 462

590 501 921 739 903 082 083 864 704 696 768 550 445 978 729 613 621 764 654 567 419 965 635 667 480 737 668 477 375 951

441 037 967 066 081 852 075 528 724 371 363 045 672 875 988 709 549 874 633 743 456 606 457 916 482 877 894 732 501 818

795 539 940 838 600 821 639 076 917 073 411 953 416 935 564 946 378 487 793 934 587 956 523 454 845 455 466 925 636 391

498 038 395 067 650 761 621 666 947 417 721 586 972 882 356 675 911 768 892 681 646 851 433 653 738 887 963 362 586 725

660 913 790 497 080 499 572 667 658 072 678 884 529 949 864 961 876 943 751 598 888 946 628 697 900 593 894 565 432 487

486 647 495 859 873 640 415 077 823 737 414 823 907 396 549 891 606 594 224 720 616 890 723 570 775 662 862 964 833 413

880 540 483 546 497 079 078 916 464 877 862 044 556 670 579 682 975 836 977 617 811 591 918 770 561 468 840 752 650 932

687 400 039 623 068 571 378 460 071 455 578 653 444 848 974 747 741 672 438 409 850 644 461 408 863 379 688 566 409 740

612 531 648 962 717 069 433 070 731 887 403 867 548 873 863 658 520 593 943 543 957 891 637 924 827 782 899 526 978 489

898 456 610 040 713 853 642 699 513 914 043 886 752 494 708 488 815 472 797 900 562 628 459 570 890 671 432 555 656 634

941 603 356 702 994 455 759 839 628 714 665 509 444 999 896 955 651 871 761 668 461 567 644 860 766 478 763 365 762 818

832 981 881 583 637 041 358 541 042 542 470 682 792 609 371 726 392 923 782 893 991 392 982 437 581 771 597 611 504 733

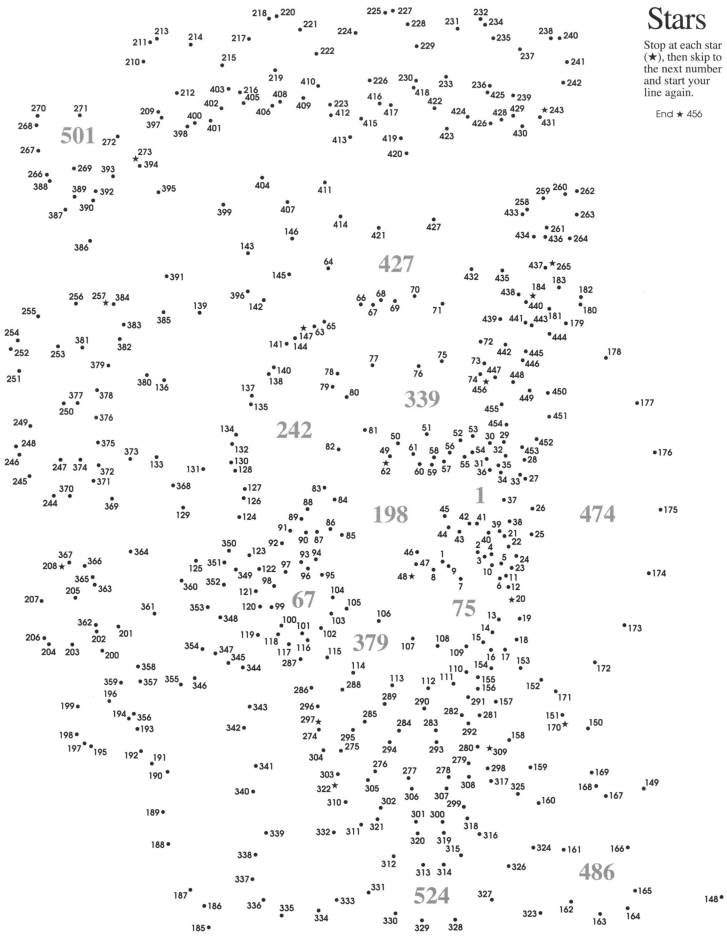

Stars

Stop at each star
(★), then skip to
the next number
and start your
line again.

End ★ 456

* Use the number clues in this puzzle
to solve the puzzle on **page 33.**

32

© 2014 Monkeying Around

Stars

Stop at each star
(★), then skip to
the next number
and start your
line again.

End ★ 540

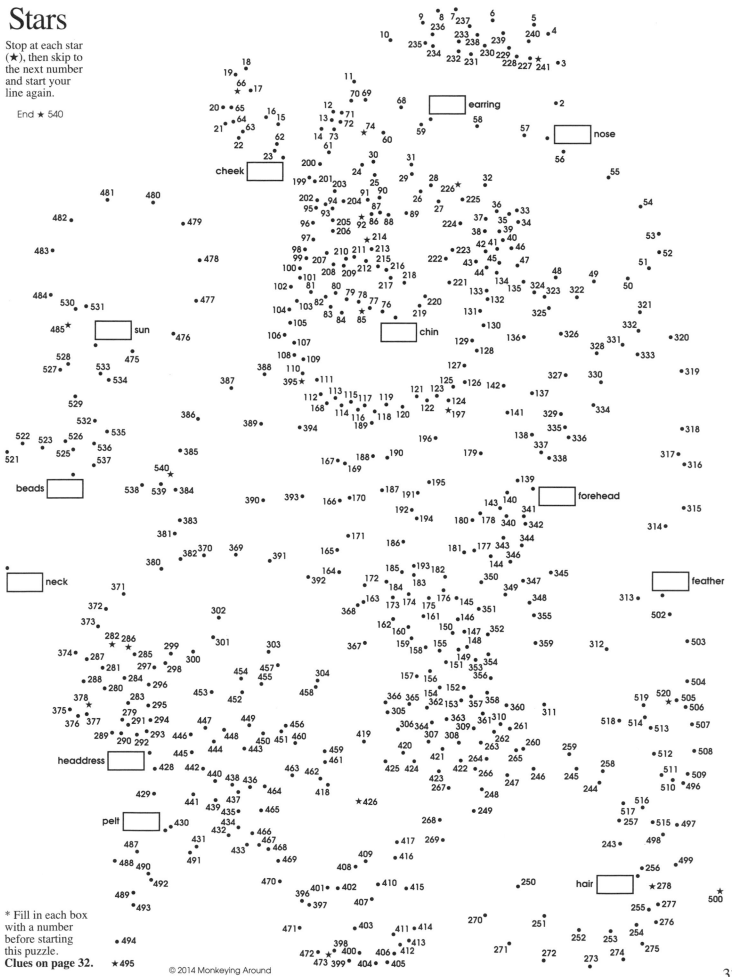

* Fill in each box
with a number
before starting
this puzzle.
Clues on page 32.

© 2014 Monkeying Around

33

* **Tip:** Long lines, use a ruler.

Stop at each star (★), then skip to the next number and start your line again.

End ★ 718

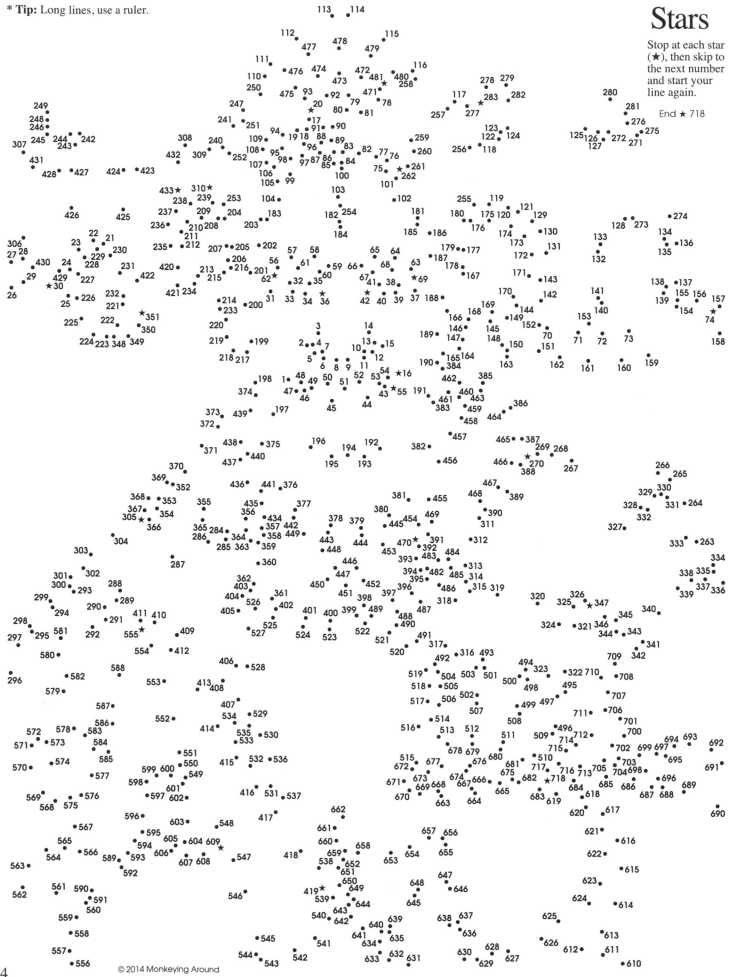

34   © 2014 Monkeying Around

No Dots!

Connect Numbers:

1 – 288
A – E

* **Tips:** Aim for the middle of each number.
Long lines, use a ruler.

35

Scene

Stop at each bean sprout (🌱), then skip to the next number and start your line again.

End 🌱 548

© 2014 Monkeying Around

After connecting the "A" set, skip to the "B" set and start your line again. Repeat for "C" set, and so on.

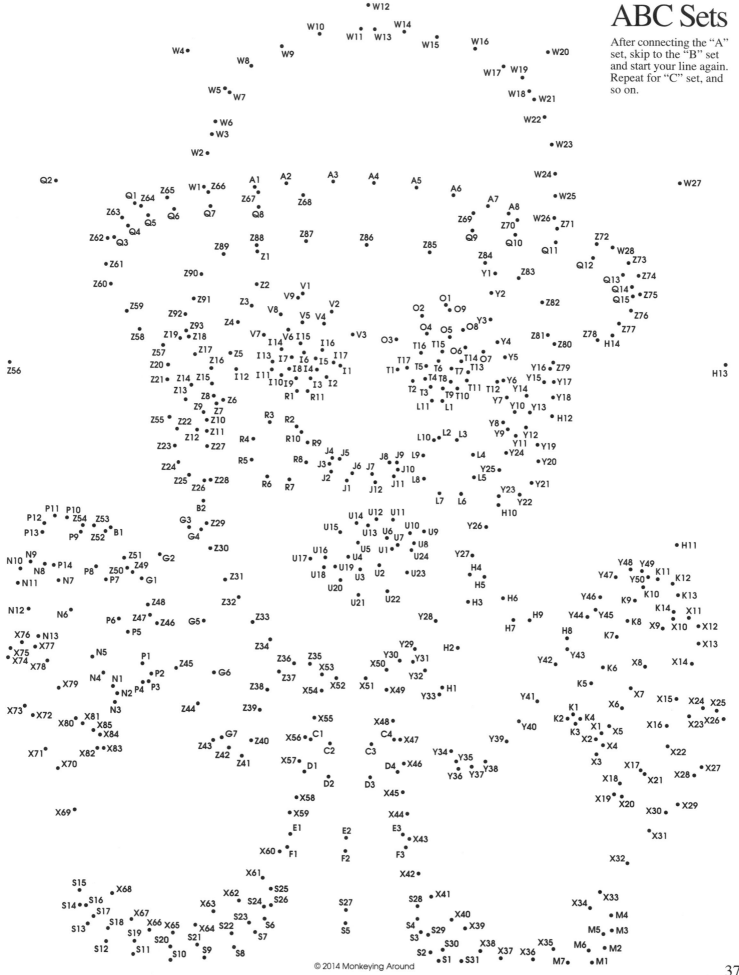

Stars

Stop at each star
(★), then skip to
the next number
and start your
line again.

End ★ 241

* **Tip:** Long lines, use a ruler.

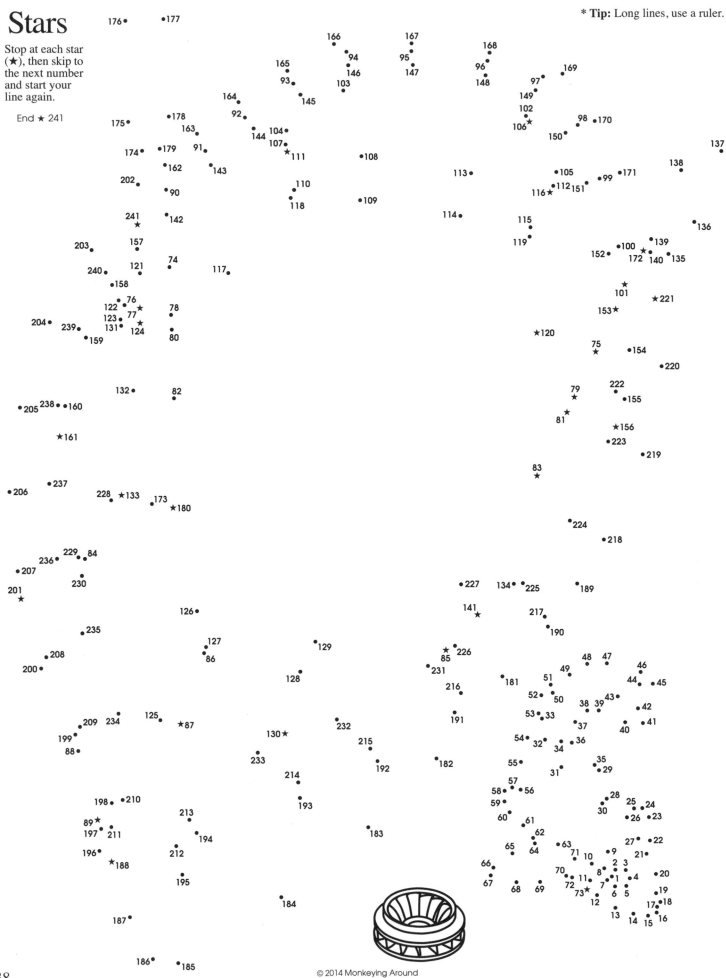

38

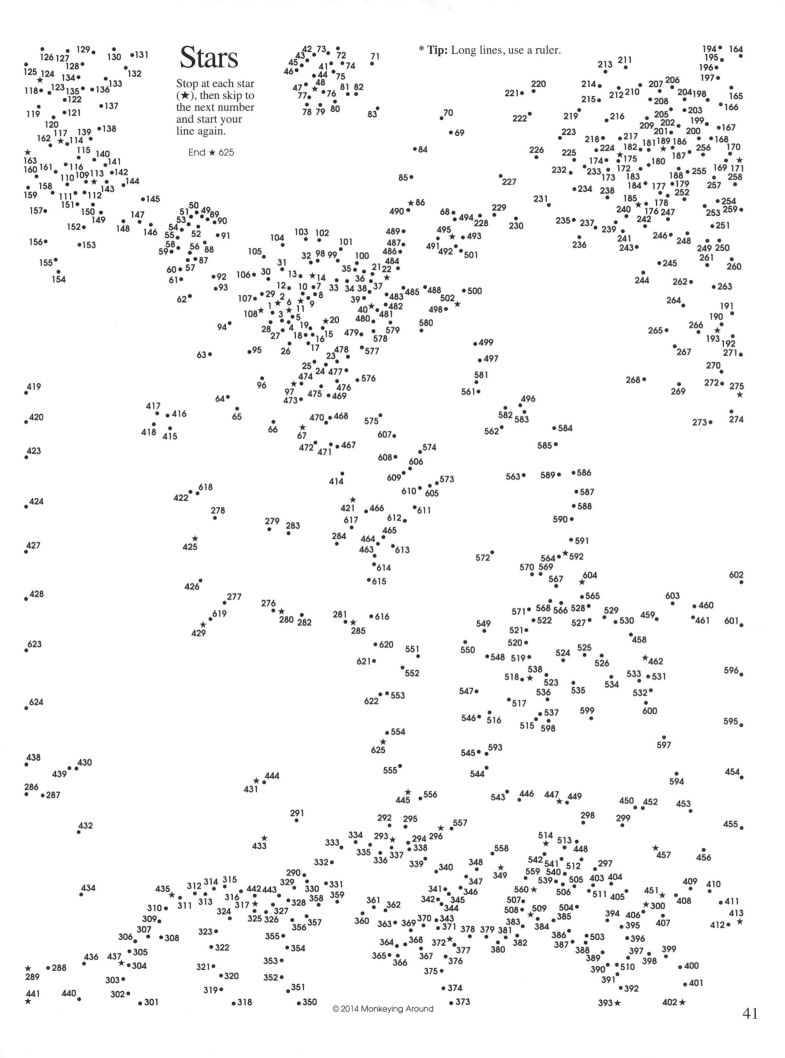

Stars

Stop at each star (★), then skip to the next number and start your line again.

End ★ 625

* **Tip:** Long lines, use a ruler.

© 2014 Monkeying Around

41

Circuits

Complete each set of circuits using straight lines. Start at a circle and end at a circle to complete each circuit.

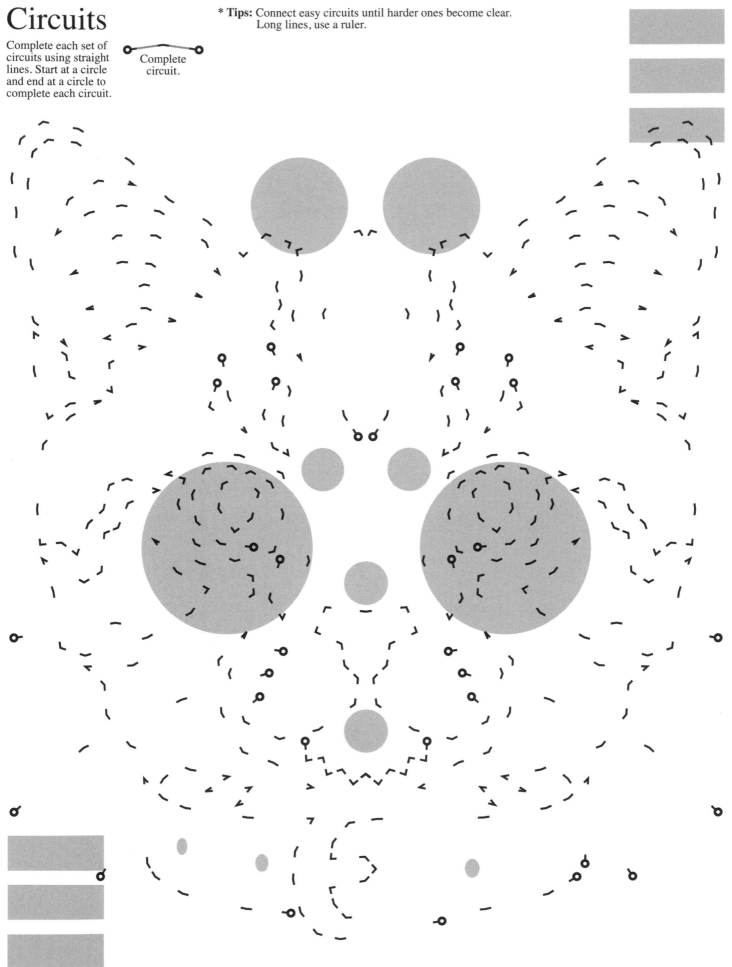

Complete circuit.

* **Tips:** Connect easy circuits until harder ones become clear. Long lines, use a ruler.

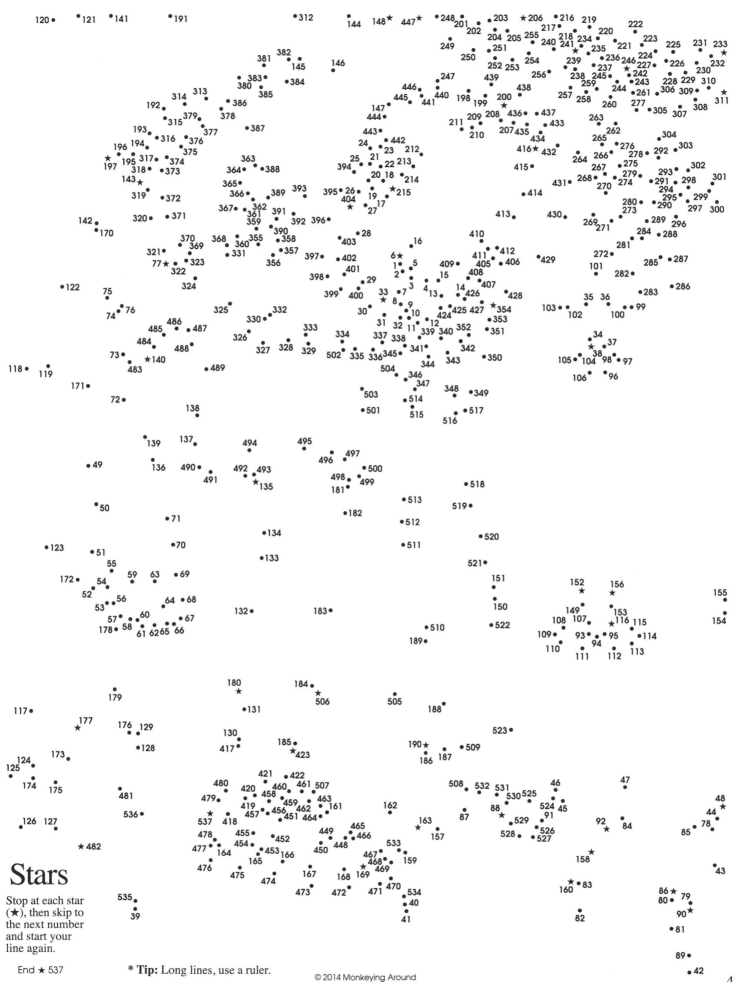

Stars

Stop at each star
(★), then skip to
the next number
and start your
line again.

* **Tip:** Long lines, use a ruler.

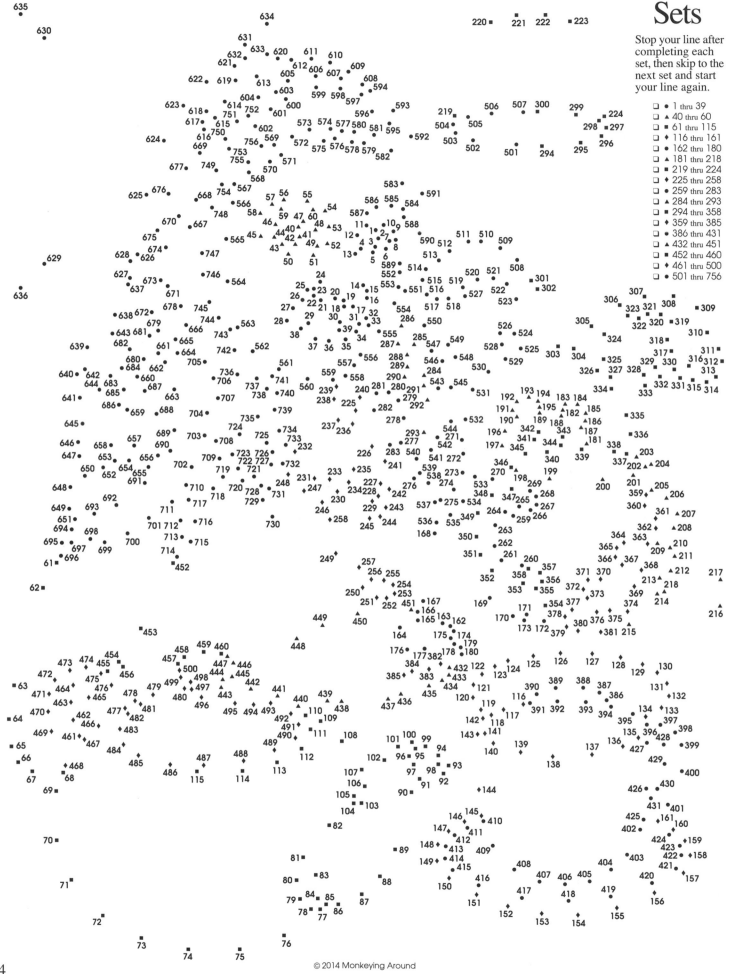

Stop your line after
completing each
set, then skip to the
next set and start
your line again.

❑ ● 1 thru 39
❑ ▲ 40 thru 60
❑ ■ 61 thru 115
❑ ◆ 116 thru 161
❑ ● 162 thru 180
❑ ▲ 181 thru 218
❑ ■ 219 thru 224
❑ ◆ 225 thru 258
❑ ● 259 thru 283
❑ ▲ 284 thru 293
❑ ■ 294 thru 358
❑ ◆ 359 thru 385
❑ ● 386 thru 431
❑ ▲ 432 thru 451
❑ ■ 452 thru 460
❑ ◆ 461 thru 500
❑ ● 501 thru 756

44

© 2014 Monkeying Around

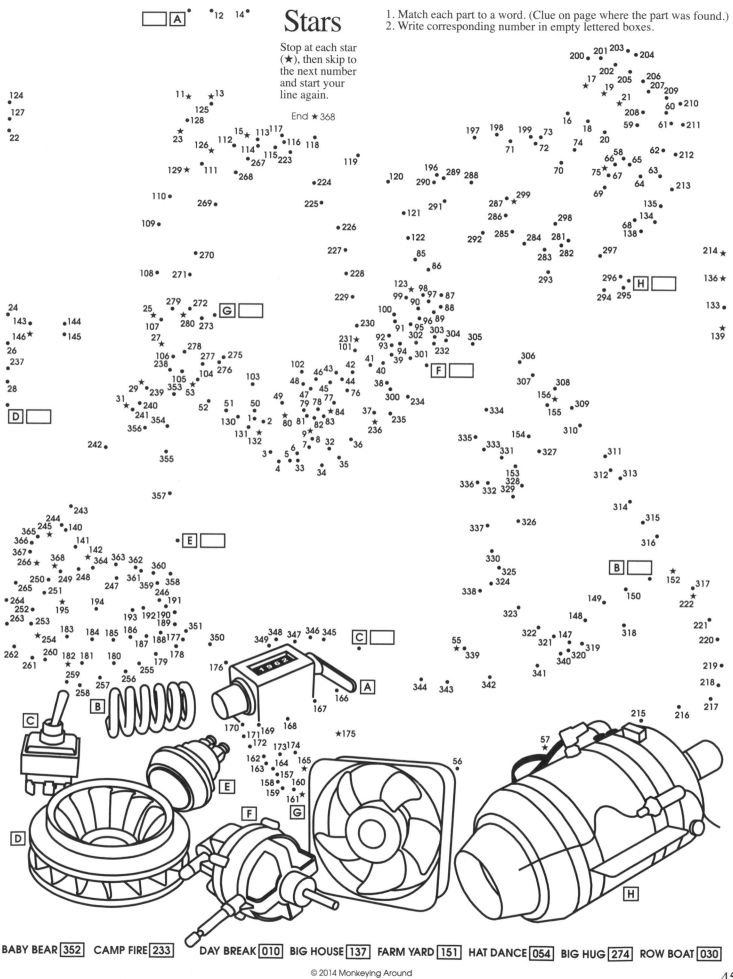

Stars

Stop at each star (★), then skip to the next number and start your line again.

End ★368

1. Match each part to a word. (Clue on page where the part was found.)
2. Write corresponding number in empty lettered boxes.

BABY BEAR 352   CAMP FIRE 233   DAY BREAK 010   BIG HOUSE 137   FARM YARD 151   HAT DANCE 054   BIG HUG 274   ROW BOAT 030

Crazy Dots

Connect Dots: